I-SPY

Radley

BIRDS

Thi

D1115075

Great Crested Grebe

This attractive bird breeds on lakes, gravel pits, and sometimes on rivers. Look out for the head tufts during the breeding season.

*I-Spy for **15***

Grey Heron

The Grey Heron is easy to recognize even in flight. It flies with slow, lazy-looking wingbeats and its long legs trail out behind. It is often mobbed by smaller birds.

*I-Spy for **15***

Moorhen

Moorhens are found in most kinds of watery areas where there are plants growing around the edges. Sometimes it may be quite shy. Look out for the red area on the front of the head and base of the beak.

I-Spy for ***10***

Coot

'As bald as a coot'! Coots are not bald but they do have a white patch on the forehead and beak. They are found on lakes, gravel pits, and reservoirs.

I-Spy for ***10***

Cormorant

These large birds nest on sea cliffs but they may be seen quite far inland on rivers. Watch out for them holding out their wings to dry after they have been diving for food.

I-Spy for ***15***

Shag

The Shag is smaller than the Cormorant and is rarely seen away from the coast. In the spring the bird boasts a crest on its head.

I-Spy for ***15***

Black-headed Gull

These common gulls are not only seen at the coast. During the winter, you can see them in most areas. Look carefully, what colour are their heads in summer?

____

______________ ☐

*I-Spy for **10***
Double with answer

Herring Gull

The Herring Gull is a large, heavily built bird with pink legs and a yellow bill bearing a bright red spot on the underside. It is found mainly at the coast. ☐

*I-Spy for **10***

Great Black-backed Gull

The Great Black-backed Gull is even bigger and more powerful looking than the Herring Gull. Even its beak is more massive and it will attack other birds.
*I-Spy for **15***

Arctic Tern

The Arctic Tern and the Common Tern are quite hard to tell apart so birdwatchers often lump them together under the name 'Comic Tern'. Look out for their bouncing flight and forked tails.
*I-Spy for **20***

Guillemot

When they sit upon rocks at the coast, these auks resemble penguins. They nest on bare ledges on sea cliffs. They are fast fliers and good swimmers.

*I-Spy for **20***

Razorbill

At a distance, it is not always easy to tell Guillemots and Razorbills apart unless they are in mixed colonies, when this bird looks blacker and rather dumpier than the Guillemot. Its bill is also quite different.

*I-Spy for **20***

Mute Swan

This bird is quite unmistakable. It has been said that it is the heaviest bird capable of flying long distances. Male and female are hard to tell apart but they are often given special names — what?

*I-Spy for **5***
Double with answer

Canada Goose

As their name suggests, these well-known geese originally came from North America but they were introduced into Europe more than 200 years ago. You can see them on lakes and ponds or in fields.

*I-Spy for **10***

Brent Goose

This goose is about the size of a large duck. They are usually seen around coastal mudflats where they feed mainly on eel grass during the winter.

*I-Spy for **25***

Shelduck

The bold colours of this bird make it easily recognizable even at a distance. It is usually found around coastal estuaries. Look out for the red knob at the base of the male's beak.

*I-Spy for **15***

Mallard

Everyone knows the Mallard. It is the bird that you always think of as a typical wild duck. Ducks and drakes look identical.
True or False?

*I-Spy for **5***
Double with answer

Tufted Duck

This black and white duck gets its name from the tuft on its head. They are found on lakes, reservoirs, and flooded gravel pits where they may occur in large numbers.
*I-Spy for **10***

Red Kite

This reddy coloured bird of prey is quite easily recognized from its 'floating' flight and the forked tail. In some areas it is rare, while in others it may be seen in small flocks.

I-Spy for ***30***

Sparrowhawk

Look out for Sparrowhawks dashing along and over hedgerows as they are trying to catch small birds by surprise. Female Sparrowhawks are larger and browner than males.

I-Spy for ***25***

Buzzard

Buzzards may be seen wheeling over mountains, moors, and other kinds of open country either singly or in small groups. Listen for their 'mewing' call.

*I-Spy for **25***

Golden Eagle

The sheer size of this bird is usually enough to give it away. It has broad wings with 'fingered' tips. Despite their size, they often feed on carrion. How does the bird get its name?

*I-Spy for **30***
Double with answer

Osprey

Ospreys are usually seen around lakes and rivers. They feed on fish which they catch by swooping down and grasping a fish from just beneath the water.

*I-Spy for **30***

Kestrel

It is easy to see why this bird gets its country name of 'Windhover'. Look out for them hovering by roads and motorways searching for insects and small mammals to pounce on.

*I-Spy for **5***

Peregrine

This fast-flying, anchor-shaped falcon feeds mainly on birds such as pigeons and doves which it catches in flight. It swoops on its victim and hits it in a cloud of feathers.

*I-Spy for **50***

Red Grouse

It is also called the Willow Grouse but they are always found on heather moorland. When disturbed, they fly low with a call which sounds like 'Go Back! Go Back!'

*I-Spy for **15***

Ptarmigan

If you are lucky enough to see a male Ptarmigan in winter, it is likely to have changed its plumage from dark brown to all white. They are found on heather moors.

*I-Spy for **30***

Black Grouse

The male and female, both with a distinctive lyre-shaped tail, are often called 'Black Cock' and 'Grey Hen'. They are found in scrubland and coniferous woods.

I-Spy for ***25***

Red-legged Partridge

This type of Partridge comes from France and Spain but has been introduced into other parts of Europe including Britain. They are found in farmland and other kinds of open country.

I-Spy for ***15***

Pheasant

The brightly coloured male Pheasant is unmistakable. These birds are found in most types of country where there are seeds and berries to feed on and trees in which to roost.

I-Spy for ***10***

Oystercatcher

With its bright red bill, red legs, red eyes and black and white plumage, the Oystercatcher is easy to recognize at the coast. Listen for its loud piping call.

*I-Spy for **10***

Ringed Plover

In the winter, these attractive little shore birds are found along muddy estuaries. For the rest of the year, look for them along sandy or shingly coasts.

*I-Spy for **15***

Lapwing

Lapwings can be seen in most kinds of open countryside including farmland. Although their upper parts are greenish, in flight they look black and white. Can you think of two other common names for this bird?

____

____

*I-Spy for **10***
Double with answer

Dunlin

These little birds are common shore birds and may be seen in large flocks. You can see them dashing about the mud probing for food with their beaks.
*I-Spy for **15***

Snipe
This long-billed bird is best known for its habit of 'drumming' during the breeding season. It flies up and then dives with its outer tail feathers spread out to make a throbbing noise.
I-Spy for ***25***

Curlew
This bird nests on moorlands and spends the rest of the year at the coast where it uses its long, curved bill to probe in the mud for food. Its name comes from its 'Cooer-leeoo' call.
I-Spy for ***25***

Redshank

This is another common wading bird and, as its name suggests, it has red legs as well as a reddish base to its bill. They feed on estuaries during the winter.

I-Spy for ***15***

Common Sandpiper

With its white underside, brownish back, and its habit of bobbing up and down when it is on the ground, this bird is quite easy to recognize.

I-Spy for ***15***

Stock Dove

Stock Doves are found in farmland, parks, the edges of woods, cliffs, ruined buildings, and even among sand dunes. They feed mainly on seeds.

*I-Spy for **15***

Wood Pigeon

When Wood Pigeons take off, they usually make a loud clapping noise from their wings as they strike together. This is thought to help them make a fast take-off.

*I-Spy for **5***

Collared Dove

With their pinkish, fawnish, grey colour and black, collar-like mark on either side of the neck, these birds are easy to recognize. They can often be seen in gardens.
*I-Spy for **5***

Turtle Dove

The Turtle Dove is a small pigeon which is usually found in open woodland. They are more often heard than seen, and make a pleasant purring sound.
*I-Spy for **25***

Cuckoo

The Cuckoo is more often heard than seen: they are sometimes mistaken for birds of prey in flight. They are best known for their habit of laying their eggs in the nests of other birds.

I-Spy for ***25***

Nightjar

The Nightjar is a night-flying bird which catches moths and other nocturnal insects in flight. Its mouth is wide and surrounded by bristles. They are also sometimes known as 'Goatsuckers'. Do you know why?

I-Spy for ***50***
Double with answer

Kingfisher

Although these birds have a striking, orange-coloured breast, when you see them in their fast flight, they look like azure-blue arrows.

*I-Spy for **20***

Hoopoe

With its curved bill, bright plumage, and large crest, the Hoopoe is a very distinctive bird in the farms, gardens, and open woods of the warm areas where it is found.

*I-Spy for **20***

Barn Owl

This is a long-winged, nighthunting bird. Its breast may be near white or rather more golden and sometimes the bird almost seems to glow in the dark. They do not hoot but screech and hiss.
*I-Spy for **20***

Little Owl

You may see Little Owls during the day sitting on a fence post looking for insects. As its name suggests, it is a small owl.
*I-Spy for **15***

Short-eared Owl

Short-eared Owls are found in open country such as moorland. The word 'ear' refers to tufts of feathers on the head of the bird.

*I-Spy for **20***

Tawny Owl

This is the woodland owl which makes the familiar hooting noise. If you see mobs of small birds seemingly attacking an ivy-covered tree, there may well be a Tawny Owl roosting there.

*I-Spy for **20***

Green Woodpecker

This brightly coloured, greenish-yellow woodpecker may even be seen in gardens. It is sometimes called the 'Yaffle' because of its laughing song. What is very noticeable about this bird's flight?

I-Spy for ***10***
Double with answer

Great Spotted Woodpecker

This black and white woodpecker has a red patch beneath its tail. It 'sings' by drumming its beak against a trunk or branch of a tree. The bird feeds on insects which it digs out from under the bark.

I-Spy for ***15***

Lesser Spotted Woodpecker

This is like a smaller version of the Great Spotted: the male bird has a red cap. The drumming song is quieter and more rapid than that of its larger cousin.

I-Spy for ***25***

Skylark

As the male bird climbs into the air on rapidly beating wings, it produces its loud, warbling song. This song is a familar sound of summer in open countryside such as farmland.
*I-Spy for **5***

Woodlark

Woodlarks are usually found in parks with scattered trees as well as woodland. The tail is shorter than that of a Skylark, and the bird usually sings as it flies from perch to perch.
*I-Spy for **15***

Crested Lark

Crested Larks are found throughout most of Europe except for the British Isles. They are found in dry sandy areas including waste land and railway sidings. They may also be seen in towns.
*I-Spy for **25***

Swallow

Familar birds of summer, Swallows feed by catching insects in flight. They will also swoop down over lakes and rivers to drink. Look out for their long tail streamers.

*I-Spy for **5***

Swift

With their long, sickle-shaped wings and fast, agile flight, these birds are well named. They seldom land if not nesting, and they even sleep on the wing!

*I-Spy for **10***

House Martin

It is the white bar at the base of the tail which will allow you to tell these birds from Swallows or Swifts. When they do not nest on houses, where would you expect them to build their nests?

*I-Spy for **5***
Double with answer

Sand Martin

In general shape, this bird looks like a House Martin but it is brown in colour above and has a white underside with a brown bar across its chest. It nests in burrows in sandy cliffs.

*I-Spy for **20***

Meadow Pipit

This small brown bird has a longish tail which it flicks as it runs along the ground. It is usually found in open grassland or moorland.

I-Spy for ***15***

Grey Wagtail

Grey Wagtails have conspicuous yellow patches on their breasts and rumps. They are found by fast-flowing streams and often nest under bridges.

I-Spy for ***20***

Pied Wagtail (White Wagtail)

In Britain, this bird is more black and white than it is in Europe, hence its name. It is often seen running along the ground in most kinds of open country. It gets its name from its habit of flicking its tail.

I-Spy for ***5***

Yellow Wagtail

Yellow Wagtails are found in damp fields and water meadows, gravel pits, wet moorland, and farmland near water. They feed on insects and other small creatures.

I-Spy for ***20***

Wren

This is a tiny bird and, although it is very common, its habit of hiding in hedges and holes in banks makes it hard to see. Its scientific name means 'cave-dweller'. For such a small bird, it has a very loud song.

*I-Spy for **15***

Golden Oriole

The male Oriole has a bright yellow body and black wings and tail. It is usually found in parks and open deciduous woodland although they can also be seen in scrubby areas.

*I-Spy for **20***

Dunnock

The Dunnock is often called the Hedge Sparrow and, although it is often seen in and around hedges, it is not related to sparrows and, if you look closely, you will see that the two birds have different beak shapes.

*I-Spy for **10***

Starling

One of the most noticeable characteristics of the Starling is that it flies arrow-straight. At dusk, Starlings are often seen in very large flocks flying to the roost site.

*I-Spy for **5***

House Sparrow

Everyone can recognize this little bird because it is found so close to houses and farms. It will feed on household scraps as well as on insects and seeds.

*I-Spy for **5***

Robin

Some books suggest that it is only the male Robin which has the familiar red breast. This is quite untrue and the sexes are almost impossible to tell apart. Robins have an autumn song and a spring song. True or False?

*I-Spy for **5***
Double with answer

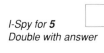

Nightingale

Its song is similar to that of the Song Thrush, but it is the long, piping sounds and melodic trills which make the song of the Nightingale so famous. It will sing during the day as well as at night.

*I-Spy for **25***

Stonechat

This black, white, and orange bird is found in heaths, commons, and moors. It gets its name from its call which sounds like two pebbles being knocked together.

I-Spy for ***15***

Wheatear

The male Wheatear is a handsome bird with his grey back, white rump, black face stripes, and orange-pink chest. These birds are found in open country such as grassland or moorland.

I-Spy for ***15***

Fieldfare

Its large size, grey head and rump, and darker end to the tail make this thrush easy to recognize. These birds breed in open woodland but gather in large flocks in farmland during the winter.

*I-Spy for **15***

Blackbird

With his shiny black plumage, yellow beak, and yellow ring round his eye, the male Blackbird is a handsome bird. The female is a dull brown colour. The male's song is musical.

*I-Spy for **5***

Song Thrush

Song Thrushes are found in gardens, woods, and hedge-rows. The brown back and speckled breast make this an easy bird to Spy. Listen to the male's song in spring; what do you notice?

*I-Spy for **5***
Double with answer

Reed Warbler

Warblers are not easy to recognize. The Reed Warbler is a small brownish bird with a paler underside. The delicate-looking bill is quite long. They nest in reed beds. Listen for the chattering song.

I-Spy for ***20***

Willow Warbler

This is another greenish-brown little bird with a paler underside. If you can see it closely, look for its pale legs, but it is the descending, musical warble with a flourish at the end which immediately identifies the bird.

I-Spy for ***15***

Chiffchaff

The Chiffchaff looks very like the Willow Warbler except that it has dark-coloured legs. But it gets its name from its song — a repetitive 'chiff-chaff, chiff-chaff'.

I-Spy for ***15***

Blackcap

As its name suggests, the male bird has a black cap on his head although that of the female is brown. Both birds are greyish brown with paler undersides, and may be seen in gardens.

I-Spy for ***15***

Whitethroat

With its brownish body, greyer head, and distinctive white throat, this little bird is one of the easier warblers to recognize. It is found in woodlands and shrubbery.

I-Spy for ***15***

Goldcrest

This is a tiny, greenish-coloured bird that is usually seen flitting from branch to branch in Larches and other coniferous trees. If you see one, look for the yellow strip with black lines on either side on the bird's head.

I-Spy for ***15***

Long-tailed Tit

With its plump little body and long tail, this delightful member of the tit family is easy to recognize. It is found in woodland and hedgerows.

I-Spy for ***10***

Marsh Tit

The Marsh Tit and Willow Tit look very similar with their black caps and, despite their names, both birds live in woodland although it is the Willow Tit that likes to be near water.

I-Spy for ***15***

Coal Tit

The Coal Tit also has a black cap but it extends down the back of its neck and this area also has a white patch in it. These birds are usually found in coniferous woodland.

I-Spy for ***15***

Crested Tit

Crested Tits are not found in southern Britain. They live in coniferous forests and are easily identified by the black and white crest on the head.

I-Spy for ***20***

Blue Tit

These little birds are familar to almost everyone, often because of their acrobatics at bird feeders and their habit of stealing the cream from milk bottles.

*I-Spy for **5***

Great Tit

With its blue-black head, white cheek patches, and yellow breast with a black bar down the centre, this is an easy bird to identify. The male's 'teacher-teacher' song is also a familiar spring sound.

*I-Spy for **5***

Chaffinch
This is a very familar bird, and the male's colours of bluish, pink, brown, green, and white stand out. The female has roughly the same pattern but the colours are duller.
*I-Spy for **5***

Greenfinch
The male bird is a bright yellowish green while the female is rather duller. Look for these birds in woodland, along hedgerows, in parks, and even in your garden.
*I-Spy for **5***

Goldfinch
The bright red, white, black, and yellow colours of this delightful little finch make it easy to recognize. It is often seen feeding on the seeds of thistle heads in autumn.
I-Spy for ***10***

Siskin
The Siskin looks rather like a Greenfinch, except that the male Siskin has a black crown and chin and rather more yellow colours on the underside. These birds eat the seeds of cones.
I-Spy for ***15***

Linnet

These birds are greyish brown above and paler on the underside but, in spring and summer, the chest of the male bird is flushed with pink. They are found in open country where there are trees and bushes.

*I-Spy for **15***

Yellowhammer

It is the bright yellow head of the male bird which is easy to spot. Listen to his song in spring and summer, as he sits atop a hedge or gate post. What does he seem to say?

*I-Spy for **10***
Double with answer

Corn Bunting

This bird is rather similar to the Yellowhammer but it lacks the bright yellow colours. Its song sounds like the rattling of bunch of keys after a 'chink-chink' start.

*I-Spy for **10***

Jay

This brightly coloured member of the Crow family is usually a shy bird and you are lucky if you see one flying between patches of woodland. Sometimes, though, they do turn up in gardens.
*I-Spy for **15***

Magpie

With its very long tail and bold black and white colours, this is an easy bird to recognize. You will often see them in the mornings feeding on the roads from animals that have been killed in the night.
*I-Spy for **5***

Jackdaw

Smaller than a Rook or a Crow and with a greyish head and rather untidy appearance, the Jackdaw is quite easy to identify. Its harsh 'keeaw' call is also very noticeable.

*I-Spy for **5***

Rook

This is a large, glossy black bird with a long bill that has a grey base. It is often found in large flocks feeding on open farmland, or in parks and gardens.

*I-Spy for **5***

Carrion Crow

This bird does not have the grey base to its bill which is also rather stouter than that of the Rook. Although it does occur in flocks, it is often seen singly.

*I-Spy for **5***

Answers

Black-headed Gull: Chocolate brown.
Mute Swan: Cobb and Penn.
Mallard: False.
Golden Eagle: from the gold-coloured feathers around the head and neck of older birds.
Lapwing: Peewit; Common Plover; Green Plover.
Nightjar: Because it was once believed that they sucked milk from she-goats.
Green Woodpecker: It is very undulating.
House Martin: On cliffs.
Robin: True.
Song Thrush: He sings a phrase and then repeats it two or three times.
Yellowhammer: 'A-little-bit-of-bread and no cheeeeese'.

© I-Spy Limited 1991

ISBN (paperback) 1 85671 003 3
ISBN (hard cover) 1 85671 004 1
Book Club edition CN1979

Michelin Tyre Public Limited Company
Davy House, Lyon Road, Harrow, Middlesex HA1 2DQ

MICHELIN and the Michelin Man are Registered Trademarks of Michelin

All rights reserved. No part of this publication may be reproduced, stored in a retrieval system, or transmitted in any form or by any means, electronic, mechanical photocopying or otherwise without the prior written permission of I-Spy Limited.

A CIP record for this title is available from the British Library.

Edited and designed by Curtis Garratt Limited, The Old Vicarage, Horton cum Studley, Oxford OX9 1BT

The Publisher gratefully acknowledges the contribution of Bruce Coleman Limited who provided all the photographs in this I-Spy book. Cover photograph:Frank Lane Picture Agency.

Colour reproduction by Norwich Litho Services Limited.

Printed in Spain.